4-Chord Songbook
More Classic Hits

WISE PUBLICATIONS
part of The Music Sales Group
London / New York / Paris / Sydney / Copenhagen / Berlin / Madrid / Tokyo

This *4-Chord Songbook* allows even beginner guitarists to play and enjoy classic songs. The songs have been specially arranged so that only 4 chords are needed to play all of the songs in the book.

The *4-Chord Songbook* doesn't use music notation. Throughout the book chord boxes are printed at the head of each song; the chord changes are shown above the lyrics. It's left to you, the guitarist, to decide on a strum pattern or picking pattern.

Some of the arrangements indicate that a capo should be used at a particular fret. This is to match the song to the key of the original recording so that you can play along; otherwise the capo is not needed for playing on your own. However, if the pitch of the vocal line is not comfortable for singing (if it is pitched too high or too low) you may wish to use a capo anyway; placing the capo behind a suitable fret will change the key of the song without learning any new chords.

Whatever you do, this *4-Chord Songbook* guarantees hours of enjoyment for guitarists of all levels, as well as providing a fine basis for building a strong repertoire.

Published by
Wise Publications
14-15 Berners Street, London W1T 3LJ, UK.

Exclusive Distributors:
Music Sales Limited
Distribution Centre, Newmarket Road, Bury St Edmunds, Suffolk IP33 3YB, UK.
Music Sales Pty Limited
120 Rothschild Avenue, Rosebery, NSW 2018, Australia.

Order No. AM988207
ISBN 978-1-84609-822-2
This book © Copyright 2007 Wise Publications,
a division of Music Sales Limited.

Printed in the EU.

www.musicsales.com

Relative Tuning

The guitar can be tuned with the aid of pitch pipes or dedicated electronic guitar tuners which are available through your local music dealer. If you do not have a tuning device, you can use relative tuning. Estimate the pitch of the 6th string as near as possible to E or at least a comfortable pitch (not too high, as you might break other strings in tuning up). Then, while checking the various positions on the diagram, place a finger from your left hand on the:

5th fret of the E or 6th string and **tune the open A** (or 5th string) to the note (A)

5th fret of the A or 5th string and **tune the open D** (or 4th string) to the note (D)

5th fret of the D or 4th string and **tune the open G** (or 3rd string) to the note (G)

4th fret of the G or 3rd string and **tune the open B** (or 2nd string) to the note (B)

5th fret of the B or 2nd string and **tune the open E** (or 1st string) to the note (E)

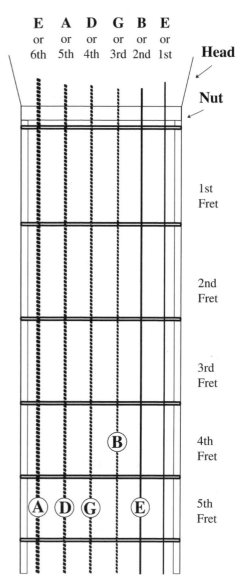

Reading Chord Boxes

Chord boxes are diagrams of the guitar neck viewed head upwards, face on as illustrated. The top horizontal line is the nut, unless a higher fret number is indicated, the others are the frets.

The vertical lines are the strings, starting from E (or 6th) on the left to E (or 1st) on the right.

The black dots indicate where to place your fingers.

Strings marked with an O are played open, not fretted. Strings marked with an X should not be played.

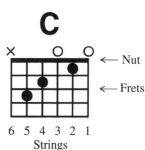

3

America

Song by Johnny Borrell & Andy Burrows
Music by Razorlight

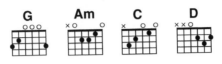

Capo 7th Fret

Intro　　|C D　|G C　|C D　|G C　|

　　　　　|C　　|G C　|C D　|G C　|

Verse 1
```
C         D
What a drag it is,
G              C
The shape I'm in.
      D
I go out somewhere,
       G          C
Then I come home again.
C         D
I light a cigarette,
G                   C
'Cause I can't get no   sleep.

There's nothing on the TV,
      D
No - thing on the radio,
      G             C
That means that much to me.
```

Chorus
```
C           D
All my life,
G           C
Watching A - merica.
            D
All my life,
G              C
There's panic in A-merica.
```

Cont.

       Am   **D**
       Oh, oh, oh,   oh!
       G   **C**
       There's trouble in A - merica.
       Am   **D**   **G**
       Oh, oh, oh,   oh.

Verse 2

       C   **D**
       Yester - day was easy,
       G   **C**
       Happiness came and went.
                 D
       I got the movie script,
               G   **C**
       But I don't know what it meant.
       C   **D**
       I light a cigarette,
              G   **C**
       Cause I can't get no   sleep.

       There's no - thing on the TV,
              D
       No - thing on the radio,
              G   **C**
       That means that much to me.

       Nothing on the TV,
              D   **G**   **C**
       No - thing on the radio, that I can believe in.

Chorus

       C   **D**
       All my life,
       G   **C**
       Watching A - merica.
              D
       All my life,
       G   **C**
       There's panic in A - merica.

Cont.

```
Am              D
    Oh, oh, oh,  oh!
G                        C
    There's trouble in A - merica.
Am              D
    Oh, oh, oh,  oh!
G                        C
    There's trouble in A - merica.
Am              D      G
    Oh, oh, oh,  oh!
```

Bridge

```
| C    D | G        | C    D | G          |
```

```
C            D
    Yester - day was easy
G                C
Yes, I got the news.
C                    D
    Oh, when you get it straight,
            G              C
You stand up you just can't lose.
                    D
    Give you my confidence,
G                C
All my faith in life.
            C
Don't stand me up,
            D
Don't let me down, no,
G                C
I need you tonight.
        C       D
To hold me,
G                    C
    Say you'll be here.
```

Cont.

```
      C          D
And hold me,
G                      C
    Say you'll be here.
      C          D
And hold me,
G            C
Say you'll be here.
C       D    G    C
Hold.
```

Chorus

```
      Am           D
   All my life
G                    C
    I'm watching A - merica
Am           D
   All my life,
G                        C
    There's panic in A - merica.
Am          D
   Oh, oh, oh,    oh!
G                    C
    She's lost in A - merica.
Am          D    G    C
   Oh, oh, oh,    oh.
                      Am    D    G    C
Tell me how does it feel?
                      Am    D    G    C
Tell me how does it feel?
                      Am    D    G
Tell me how does it feel?
```

Outro

```
| C  D   | G  C    | C  D   | G   C    |
| C  D   | G  C    | C  D   | G   C    |
  | G    C  | G    C  | G    C ‖
```

7

Big Yellow Taxi

Words & Music by
Joni Mitchell

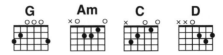

Capo 9th Fret

Intro | C | C | D | D |

| G | G | G | G ||

Verse 1

      C   G
They paved paradise and put up a parking lot

      C
With a pink hotel,

      D   G
A boutique and a swinging hot-spot.

Chorus 1

      G
Don't it always seem to go

             C   Am   G
That you don't know what you've got   till it's gone.

      C   D   G
They paved paradise, put up a parking lot.

Choo ba ba ba ba, choo ba ba ba ba.

Verse 2

      C   G
They took all the trees and put them in a tree museum

      C
And they charged the people

      D   G
A dollar and a half just to see 'em.

Chorus 2   As Chorus 1

Verse 3
```
        C                                    G
Hey farmer, farmer, put away that DDT now,
          C
Give me spots on apples
       D                    G
But leave me the birds and the bees, please!
```

Chorus 3   As Chorus 1

Verse 4
```
        C                                G
Late last night I heard the screen door slam
             C
And a big yellow taxi
D                 G
Took away my old man.
```

Chorus 4   As Chorus 1

Chorus 5
```
           G                G
I said, don't it always seem to go
              C                        Am          G
That you don't know what you've got   till it's gone.
          C            D          G
They paved paradise, put up a parking lot.

Choo ba ba ba ba,
          C            D          G
They paved paradise, put up a parking lot.

Choo ba ba ba ba.
          C            D          G      | G      ‖
They paved paradise, put up a parking lot.
```

9

Driftwood

Words & Music by
Fran Healy

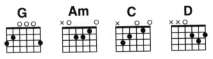

G   Am   C   D

Capo 2nd Fret

Intro | Am | D | Am | D   ‖

Verse 1
G   C   D
Everything is open, nothing is set in stone
G   C   D
Rivers turn to oceans, oceans tide you home
G   C   D
Home is where the heart is, but your heart had to roam
G   C   D
Drifting over bridges, never to return
(D)
Watching bridges burn.

Chorus 1
G   D   Am
You're driftwood floating underwater
                    C
Breaking into pieces, pieces, pieces
G   D   Am
Just driftwood, hollow and of no use
                    C
Waterfalls will find you, bind you, grind you.

Verse 2
G   C   D
Nobody is an island, everyone has to go
G   C   D
Pillars turn to butter, butter flying low
G   C   D
Low is where your heart is, but your heart has to grow
G   C   D
Drifting under bridges, never with the flow.

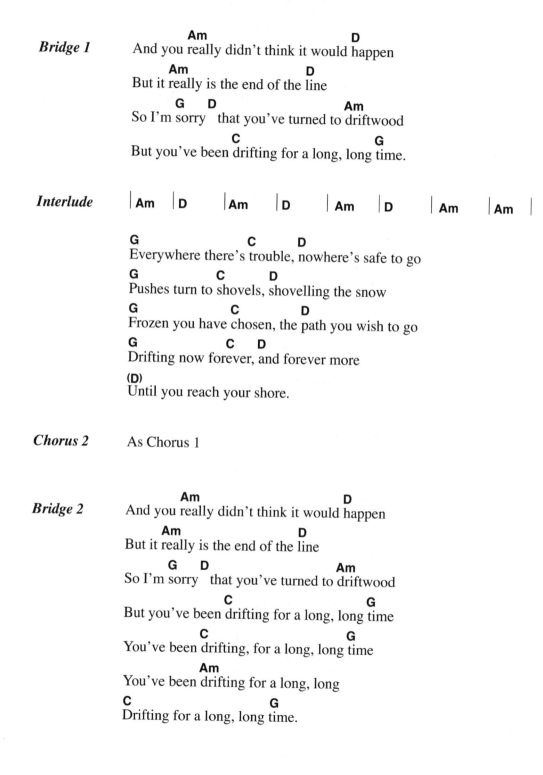

Bridge 1

       Am   D
And you really didn't think it would happen

       Am   D
But it really is the end of the line

    G   D   Am
So I'm sorry   that you've turned to driftwood

                C   G
But you've been drifting for a long, long time.

Interlude | Am | D | Am | D | Am | D | Am | Am |

                    G   C   D
Everywhere there's trouble, nowhere's safe to go

G   C   D
Pushes turn to shovels, shovelling the snow

G   C   D
Frozen you have chosen, the path you wish to go

G   C D
Drifting now forever, and forever more

(D)
Until you reach your shore.

Chorus 2   As Chorus 1

Bridge 2

       Am   D
And you really didn't think it would happen

       Am   D
But it really is the end of the line

    G   D   Am
So I'm sorry   that you've turned to driftwood

                C   G
But you've been drifting for a long, long time

                C   G
You've been drifting, for a long, long time

           Am
You've been drifting for a long, long

C   G
Drifting for a long, long time.

Bankrobber

Words & Music by
Mick Jones & Joe Strummer

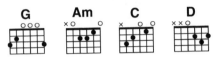

Intro | G | G | G | Am G |
| G | C D | C D | G ||

Chorus 1

G
My daddy was a bankrobber,
                Am G
But he never hurt no - body.
            C   D
He just loved to live that way,
     C   D   G
And he loved to steal your   money.

Verse 1

G
Some is rich, and some is poor,
              Am   G
That's the way the world is.
                C   D
But I don't believe in lying back,
C   D   G
Sayin' how bad your   luck is.
G
So we came to jazz it up,
              Am G
We never loved a shovel.
              C   D
Break your back to earn your pay,
     C   D   G
An' don't for - get to   grovel.

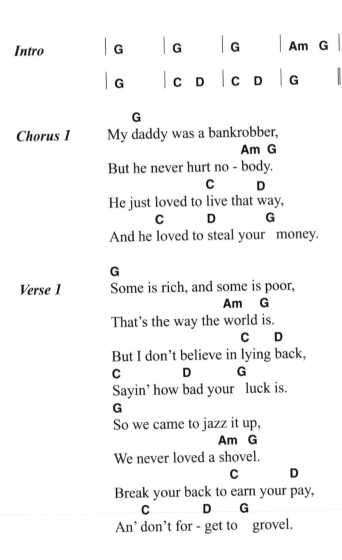

Chorus 2

G
Daddy was a bankrobber

                      Am G
But he never hurt no - body

                C   D
He just loved to live that way

           C   D   G
And he loved to take your money

Link 1

‖: G | G | G | Am G |

| G | C D | C D | G   :‖

Verse 2

         G
The old man spoke up in a bar

                 Am   G
Said I never been in prison

               C   D
A lifetime serving one ma - chine

     C   D   G
Is ten times worse than   prison

G
Imagine if all the boys in jail

                 Am G
Could get out now to - gether

                             C   D
Whadda you think they'd want to say to us?

C   D G
While we was being clever

G
Someday you'll meet your rocking chair

                Am G
Cos that's where we're spinning

                       C   D
There's no point to wanna comb your hair

C   D   G
When it's grey and thinning

Link 2

‖: G | G | G | Am G |

| G | C D | C D | G   :‖

| *Chorus 3* | As Chorus 1 |

| *Verse 3* | **G**
So we came to jazz it up,
　　　　　　　Am　G
We never loved a shovel.
　　　　　　　　　　C　　　　　　**D**
Break your back to earn your pay,
　　　C　　　　**D**　　**G**
An' don't for - get to　grovel. Hey! |

| **G** | | **G** | | **G** | | **Am** **G** | **G** | | **C** **D** | **C** **D** | **G** | |

G
Get a - way, get away, get away, get away,
　　　　　　　　　　　　　　Am　**G**
Get away, get away, get away.

| **G** | | **C** **D** | **C** **D** | **G** | ‖

| *Chorus 4* | As Chorus 2 |

| **G** | | **G** | | **G** | | **Am** **G** | **G** | | **C** **D** | **C** **D** | **G** | ‖
Run rabbit run…

| *Verse 4* | **G**
Strike out boys, for the hills.
　　　　　　　C　　　　　　**D**
I can't find that hole in the wall
　　　C　　　　　**D**　**G**
And I know that they never　will. |

| *Chorus 5* | As Chorus 2 |

| | *Fade out* |

14

Girl From Mars

Words & Music by
Tim Wheeler

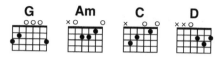

Capo 2nd Fret

Chorus 1

G   D   C
Do you remember the time I knew a girl from Mars?

   Am
I don't know if you knew that.

G   D
Oh, we'd stay up late playing cards,

          C
Henry Winterman cigars,

      Am   C
And she never told me her name,

    D   G
I still love you the girl from Mars.

Verse 1

       C D   C   Am
Sitting in a dreamy daze by the water's edge,

C   D   G
On a cool summer night.

       C D   C   Am
Fireflies and stars in the sky, (Gentle glowing light,)

C   D G
From your cigarette.

        D   C Am
The breeze blowing softly on my face

   C   D   G
Reminds me of something else.

          D   C   Am
Something that in my mem'ry has been misplaced

C   D   Am
Suddenly all comes back.

C   D   G
And as I look to the stars,

Chorus 2

                                              D   **C**

D   **C**
I remember the time I knew a girl from Mars

    Am
I don't know if you knew that.

G   **D**
Oh, we'd stay up late playing cards,

         C
Henry Winterman cigars,

    Am   **C**
And she never told me her name,

    D   **G**
I still love you the girl from Mars.

Verse 2

          C D   **C**   **Am**
Surging through the darkness (over the moon-lit strand),

   C   **D** **G**
Electricity in the air.

       C D   **C**   **Am**
Twisting all__ through the night on the terrace

C   **D**   **G**
Now that summer is here.

       C **D**   **C**   **Am**
I know that you are almost in love with me

    C   **D** **G**
I can see it in your eyes.

        D   **C** **Am**
Strange lights shimmering under the sea tonight,

     C   **D**   **Am**
And it almost blows my mind.

C   **D**   **G**
And as I look to the stars,

Chorus 3   As Chorus 2

Solo　　　‖: G　C | D　　　| C　Am | Am　:‖ *Play 4 times*

Verse 3

G　　　D　　　　D　　　　　Am
　Today I sleep in the chair by the window,
　C　　　D　　　G
It felt as if you'd returned
　　　　　　D　　　　D　　　Am
I thought that you were standing over me,
　　　C　　　　　D　　　Am
When I woke there was no-one there.
　　　C　　　D　　G
I still love you girl__ from Mars,

Chorus 4

(G)　　　　　　　　　D　　　　　　　C
Do you remember the time I knew a girl from Mars?
　　Am
I don't know if you knew that.
G　　　　　　　　　D
Oh, we'd stay up late playing cards,
　　　　　　　　C
Henry Winterman cigars,
　　　Am　　　　　G
And she never told me her name.

Chorus 5

(G)　　　　　　　　D　　　　　　C
Do you remember the time I knew a girl from Mars?
　　Am
I don't know if you knew that.
G　　　　　　　　D
Oh, we'd stay up late playing cards,
　　　　　　　C
Henry Winterman cigars,
　　Am　　　　　C
And I'll still dream of you,
　　D　　　　G
I still love you girl from Mars.

In Between Days

Words & Music by
Robert Smith

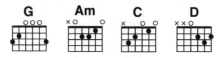

G   Am   C   D

Capo 2nd Fret

Intro   ‖: G | C | G | C :‖: G | C | G | C :‖

| Am | D | Am | D | ‖: G | C | G | C :‖

Verse 1
G   C
Yesterday I got so old
G   C
I felt like I could die;
G   C
Yesterday I got so old
 G   C
It made me want to cry.
      G   C
Go on, go on, just walk away,
      G   C
Go on, go on, your choice is made.
      G   C
Go on, go on, and disappear.
                    C
Go on, go on, away from here.

Chorus 1
               Am
Gnd I know I was wrong
            D
When I said it was true
        Am   D
That it couldn't be me and be her inbetween
              G   C   G   C
Without you, without you.

Link | G | C | G | C ‖

Verse 2

   G   D
Yesterday I got so scared
    G   D
I shivered like a child;
   G   D
Yesterday away from you
    G   D
It froze me deep inside.
           G   D
Come back, come back, don't walk away.
           G   D
Come back, come back, come back today.
           G   D
Come back, come back, why can't you see.
           G   D
Come back, come back, come back to me.

Chorus 2

           Am
And I know I was wrong
           D
When I said it was true
           Am   D
That it couldn't be me and be her inbetween
        G   D   G   D
Without you, without you,
        G   D   G   D
Without you, without you.

Coda

‖: G | D | G | D   :‖
               G   D   G   D
‖: Without you, without you.   :‖

Knockin' On Heaven's Door

Words & Music by
Bob Dylan

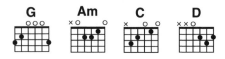

Intro

| G D | Am | G D | C |

| G D | Am | G D | C   ‖

Verse 1

G   D   Am
Mama, take this badge off of me

G   D   C
I can't use it anymore.

G   D   Am
It's gettin' dark, too dark to see

G   D   C
I feel like I'm knockin' on heaven's door.

Chorus 1

G   D   Am
Knock, knock, knockin' on heaven's door,

G   D   C
Knock, knock, knockin' on heaven's door,

G   D   Am
Knock, knock, knockin' on heaven's door,

G   D   C
Knock, knock, knockin' on heaven's door.

Verse 2

```
          G                D               Am
          Mama, put my guns in the ground
          G         D           C
          I can't shoot them anymore.
          G                D               Am
          That long black cloud is comin' down
          G               D                    C
          I feel like I'm knockin' on heaven's door.
```

Chorus 2

```
          G                D                  Am
          Knock, knock, knockin' on heaven's door,
          G               D                   C
          Knock, knock, knockin' on heaven's  door,
          G               D                   Am
          Knock, knock, knockin' on heaven's door,
          G               D                  C
          Knock, knock, knockin' on heaven's door.
```

Coda |ᐦ G D | Am | G D | C   ‖ *Fade out*

Like A Rolling Stone

Words & Music by
Bob Dylan

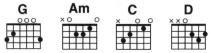

Capo 5th Fret

Intro | G | G   C | G   C | G   C ||

Verse 1
G   Am
Once upon a time you dressed so fine
          G   C   D | D |
You threw the bums a dime in your prime,   didn't you?
G   Am   G
People'd call, say "Beware, doll, you're bound to fall,"
                    C   D | D |
You thought they were all   kiddin' you
C   D
    You used to   laugh about
C   D
    Ev'rybody that was   hangin' out.
C   G   Am   G
    Now you don't talk so loud
C   G   Am   G
    Now you don't seem so proud
Am   C   D | D
About having to be scrounging for your next meal.

Chorus 1
          G   C   D
How does it feel
          G   C   D
How does it feel
                    G   C   D
To be without a home
                        G   C   D
Like a complete unknown
                    G   C   D
Like a rolling stone?

Link 1 | G   C | D | D ||

Verse 2

       G   Am   G
You've   gone to the finest school alright, Miss Lonely

        C   D | D |
But you know you only used to get juiced in it

    G   Am   G
Nobody ever taught you how to live out on the street

                 C   D | D |
And now you're gonna have to get used to it

C   D
   You said you'd never compromise

C   D
   With the mystery tramp, but now you realise

C   G   Am G
   He's not selling any alibis __

C   G   Am G
As you stare into the vacuum of his eyes

       Am   C   D | D |
And ask him do you want to   make a deal?

Chorus 2

         G   C D
How does it feel

         G   C D
How does it feel

           G   C D
To be on your own

            G   C D
With no direction home

          G   C D
A complete unknown

         G   C D
Like a rolling stone?

Link 2 | G   C | D | D ||

Verse 3

    G   Am
You   never turned around to see the frowns

G   C
   On the jugglers and the clowns

                      D | D |
When they all come down and did tricks for you

    G   Am
You never understood that it ain't no good

    G   C   D | D |
You shouldn't let other people get your kicks for you

cont.

C   D
You used to ride on the chrome horse with your diplomat

C   D
Who carried on his shoulder a Siamese cat

C   G   Am   G
Ain't it hard when you discover that

C   G   Am   G
He really wasn't where it's at

Am
After he took from you everything

C   D | D
He could steal. ⎯

Chorus 3   As Chorus 2

Link 3 | G C | D | D ||

Verse 4

G   Am   G
Princess on the steeple and all the pretty people

               C   D | D |
They're all drinkin', thinkin' that they got it made

G   Am
Exchanging all kinds of precious gifts and things

G   C
But you'd better take your diamond ring

D
You'd better pawn it babe | D |

C   D
You used to be so amused

C   D
At Napoleon in rags and the language that he used

C   G   Am   G
Go to him now, he calls you, you can't refuse,

C   G   Am   G
When you got nothing, you got nothing to lose

Am
You're invisible now, you got no secrets

C   D | D
To conceal. ⎯

Chorus 4   As Chorus 2

Coda ||: G C | D | G C | D   :|| *Repeat to fade*

(Looking For)
The Heart Of Saturday Night

Words & Music by
Tom Waits

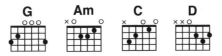

Capo 2nd Fret

Intro | G | G | C | C |

| Am | D | G | G ||

Verse 1
           G
Well you gassed her up behind the wheel,

        C
With your arm around your sweetheart,

In your Oldsmobile,

Am
Barrelin' down the boulevard,

D   **G**
Looking for the heart of Saturday night.

Verse 2
        G
You got paid on Friday

And your pockets are jinglin'

  C
You see the lights

You get all a tinglin'

          Am
'Cause you're cruisin' with a six

   D   **G**
You're looking for the heart of Saturday night.

Bridge

       Am
Now you combed your hair,

D
Shaved your legs,

G
   Tryin' to wipe out ev'ry trace,

      Am
Of all the other days in the week,

D
This'll be the Saturday you're reachin' your peak.

Verse 3

       G
You're stoppin' on the red,

Goin' on the green,

      C
'Cause to - night'll be like nothin'

That you've ever seen,

       Am
And you're barrelin' down the boulevard.

D   **G**
Lookin' for the heart of Saturday night.

Interlude

| **G** | **G** | **C** | **C** | |
| **Am** | **D** | **G** | **G** | ‖ |

Bridge

      Am   **D**
Is it the crack of the poolballs, or the neon buzzin'?

       G
And the telephone's ringin',

It's your second cousin

      Am
The barmaid is smilin' from the corner of her eye

      D
She's got the magic of a melancholy tear in her eye.

Verse 4
```
             G
And it makes you kind of special down in the core,
                   C
'Cause you're dreamin' of the Saturdays that came before
            Am
And they've got you stumblin'
D                G
  Onto the heart of Saturday night.
```

Verse 5
```
             G
So you gassed her up,

Behind the wheel,
            C
With your arm around your sweet one,

In your Oldsmobile.
Am
Barrelin' down the boulevard,
D                     G
Looking for the heart of Saturday night.
```

Outro
```
            Am
You go barrelin' down the boulevard,
D                     G
Looking for the heart of Saturday night.
            Am
You go barrelin' down the boulevard,
D                     G            | G        |
Looking for the heart of Saturday night.

| C        | C        | Am      | D      | G       | G       |
```

Love Is All Around

Words & Music by
Reg Presley

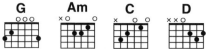

Capo 7th Fret

Intro | D C | D C | D G | D

Verse 1
G   Am C   D   G Am | C D
I feel it in my fingers, I feel it in my toes,
G   Am   C   D   G Am | C D
The love that's all around me, and so the feeling grows,
G   Am C   D   G Am | C D
It's written on the wind, it's everywhere I go,
G   Am   C   D G Am | C D | D || C
So if you really love me, come on and let it show.

Chorus 1
                        Am   C
You know I love you, I always will,
                          G
My mind's made up by the way I feel.
         C   Am
There's no beginning, there'll be no end,
                     D
'Cause on my love you can depend.

Instrumental | G Am | C D | G Am | C D

Verse 2
G   Am C   D   G Am | C D
I see your face before me as I lay on my bed,
G   Am   C   D   G Am | C D
I cannot get to thinking of all the things you said.
G   Am C   D   G Am | C D
You gave your promise to me and I gave mine to you,
G   Am   C   D   G Am | C D | D || C
I need someone beside me in everything I do.

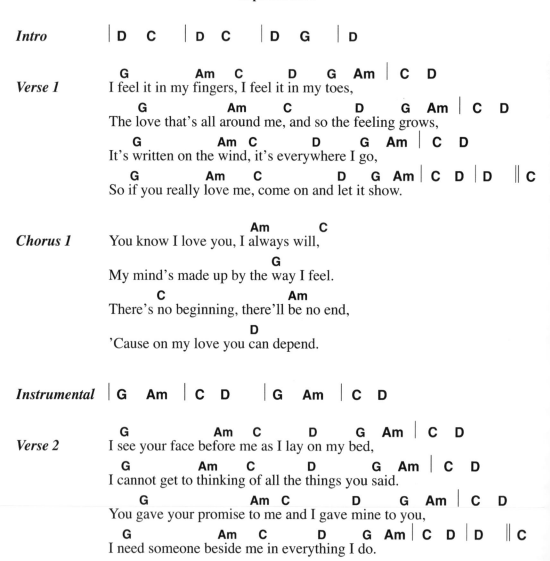

Chorus 2

  (C)   **Am**   **C**
You know I love you, I always will,

                      G
My mind's made up by the way I feel.

       C   **Am**
There's no beginning, there'll be no end,

               C   **C** **G** | C G | C
'Cause on my love you can depend.

          G   **C**
Got to keep it moving.

Verse 3

       G   **Am** **C**   **C**   **G** **Am** | C
It's written in the wind, oh, everywhere I go,

  G   **Am C**   **C**   **G** **Am** | C
So if you really love me, come on and let it show,

  C
Come on and let it (show).

  G   **Am**
‖: Come on and let it,

C   **C**
Come on and let   it,

G   **Am C**   **C**
Come on and let it show.   :‖ *Repeat to fade*

Mad World

Words & Music by
Roland Orzabal

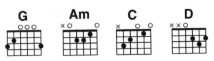

Capo 8th Fret

Intro ‖ Am │ D │ Am │ D ‖

Verse 1
Am   **C**
   All around me are fa - miliar faces,
G   **D**
   Worn out places, worn out faces.
Am   **C**
   Bright and early for their daily races
G   **D**
Going nowhere, going nowhere.

Verse 2
Am   **C**
   The tears are filling up their glasses,
G   **D**
No expression, no expression.
Am   **C**
   Hide my head I wanna drown my sorrow,
G   **D**
No tomorrow, no tomorrow.

Chorus 1
Am   **D**
   And I find it kind of funny,
                Am
I find it kind of sad,
              D   **Am**
The dreams in which I'm dying are the best I've ever had.
              D
I find it hard to tell you,
              Am
I find it hard to take,
              D
When people run in circles it's a very, very,
Am   **D** **Am**   **D**
   Mad world,   mad world.

Verse 3

    Am   **C**
    Children waiting for the day they feel good,

G   **D**   **Am**
Happy birthday, happy birth - day,

                      C
And I feel the way that every child should,

G   **D**   **Am**
Sit and listen, sit and list - en.

Verse 4

                      C
Went to school and I was very nervous

G   **D**
No one knew me, no one knew me.

Am   **C**
    Hello teacher tell me what's my lesson,

G   **D**
Look right through me, look right through me.

Chorus 2   As Chorus 1

Outro

    Am   **D**
    Enlargen your world

Am   **D**
    Mad   world.

Same Jeans

Words & Music by
Kyle Falconer & Keiren Webster

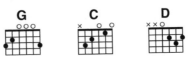

Capo 5th Fret

Intro | G   C | D   G | G   C | D   G

Verse 1
                  G   C   D   G
I've had the same jeans on   for four days now,
            G   C   D   G
I'm gonna go to a disco in the middle of the town.
            G   C   D   G
Ev'rybo - dy's dressing up, I'm dressing down.

| G   C | D   G

Verse 2
G   C   D   G
Life's one big circle and it does end,
            G C   D   G
When it ends will you still be my friend?
G   C   D   G
Am I making a fool of my - self? Oh, tell me,
G   C   D   G
I'm not making a fool of my - self.

Chorus
           G   C   G C
So, when you look in the mirror,
           G   C   D
Re - flecting back at you   someone that you don't know.
G   C   G   C
    That shit's made your head   spin around,
          G   C   D
So get yourself togeth - er and get your feet back on the ground.

Verse 3   As Verse 1

Verse 4

       G   C   D   G
I take my hat(s) off to the   busker man,

           G   C   D   G
When he drowns   all his sor - rows on singin' a song,

      G   C   D   G
Not ev - 'rything   has worked out to plan,

        G   C   D   G
But believe   me he's smiling as long as he can.

Chorus 2   As Chorus 1

Solo ||: G   C | G   C | G   C | D5   :||

              | D |
            (I've had the)

Verse 5   As Verse 1

Verse 6

       G   C   D   G
My mind's not perfect but it's sin - cere,

          G   C   D   G
You'd be a - mazed at what you can achieve   in a year.

         G C   D   G
Now you tried so hard, but your heart's   on a switch.

        G   C   D   G
And I know you try so hard, But your heart's   on a switch.

Chorus 3 ||: As Chorus 1 :||

Interlude | G   C | D   G | G   C G | C | G   C G |

Outro

         G   C
||: Same Jeans on for four   days now,

         G   C
Ev'ry - body's dressing up I'm dress - ing down,

G   C
Am I making a fool   of myself,

        G   C
Now be - lieve me lady, I can't tell. :||

| G   C | G   C | G   C | D G ||

She Said She Said

Words & Music by
John Lennon & Paul McCartney

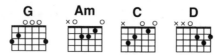

Capo 8th Fret

Intro | D | D   ‖

Verse 1
    D   **C** **G**
She said, _____

                D   **C** **G**
'I know what it's like to be dead.

            D   **C** **G**
I know what it is to be sad.'

          D   **C**   **G**   **D**
And she's making me feel like I've never been born.

| D C | G D ‖

Verse 2
    D   **C** **G**
I said, _____

              D   **C** **G**
'Who put all those things in your head?

             D   **C** **G**
Things that make me feel that I'm mad,

          D   **C**   **G**   **D**
And you're making me feel like I've never been born.'

| D C | G D ‖

Bridge 1
    D   **C**   **D**
She said, 'You don't understand what I said.'

      C   **D**
I said, 'No, no, no, you're wrong.

          Am   **D**
When I was a boy

            G   **D**   **G**
Everything was right,   everything was right.'

Verse 3

      D   **C** **G**
I said, _____

                  D   **C**   **G**
'Even though you know what you know,

         D   **C**   **G**
I know that I'm ready to leave,

          D   **C**   **G**   **D**
'Cause you're making me feel like I've never been born.'

| **D**   **C** | **G**   **D** | ‖

Bridge 2

      D   **C**   **D**
She said, 'You don't understand what I said.'

         C   **D**
I said, 'No, no, no, you're wrong.

             Am   **D**
When I was a boy

          G   **D**   **G**
Everything was right,   everything was right.'

Verse 4

      D   **C** **G**
I said, _____

                  D   **C**   **G**
'Even though you know what you know,

         D   **C**   **G**
I know that I'm ready to leave,

          D   **C**   **G**   **D**
'Cause you're making me feel like I've never been born.'

| **D**   **C** | **G**   **D** | ‖

Coda

D
She said, (she said,)

'I know what it's like to be dead,'

(I know what it's like to be dead,)

'I know what it is to be sad,'

(I know what it is to be sad,)

'I know what it's like to be dead.' *Fade out*

Somebody To Love

Words & Music by
Darby Slick

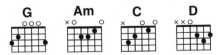

Verse 1

             Am   D   G   Am
When the truth is found   to be ___ lies

              D   G   Am
And all the joy   within you ___ dies.

Chorus 1

N.C.   C   G   Am
Don't you want somebody to love,

D   C   G   Am
Don't you need somebody to love;

D   C   G   Am
Wouldn't you love somebody to love,

D   G   D
You'd better find somebody to (love.)

Link 1

| Am | D | Am | G | Am | Am |
love.

Verse 2

             Am   D G   Am   G
When the garden flowers,   they are ___ dead, yes,

       Am   D G   Am   D
And your mind, your mind, is so full of red.

Chorus 2

G   C   G   Am
Don't you want somebody to love,

D   C   G   Am
Don't you need somebody to love;

D   C   G   Am
Wouldn't you love somebody to love,

D   G   D   Am
You'd better find somebody to love.

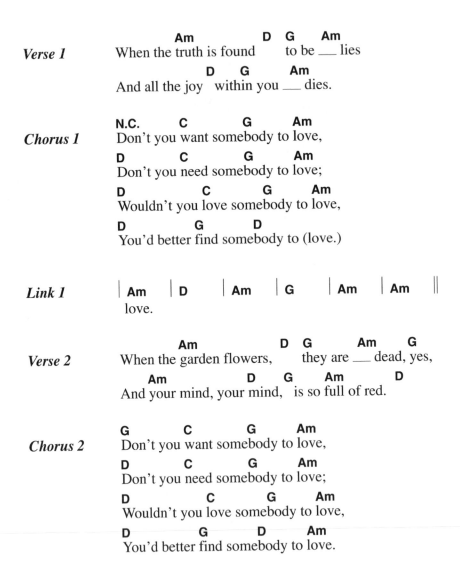

Verse 3

N.C.   G   D
Your eyes, I say your eyes may look like his, ____

                 Am   D
Yeah, but in your head, baby,

         G   Am   C
I'm afraid you don't know where it is.

Chorus 3

D   C   G   Am
Don't you want somebody to love,

D   C   G   Am
Don't you need somebody to love;

D   C   G   Am
Wouldn't you love somebody to love,

D   G   D
You'd better find somebody to (love.)

Link 2

| Am | G | D | C | Am | Am ‖
love.

Verse 4

Am   D   G   Am   C   G
Tears are running   all round and round your breast,

        Am   D   G   Am   C
And your friends, baby,   they treat you like a guest. ___

Chorus 4

G   C   G   D
Don't you want somebody to love,

            C   G   D
Don't you need somebody to love;

                C   G   D
Wouldn't you love somebody to love,

            G   D   Am   D
You'd better find somebody to love. _____

Coda

| Am | Am ‖ Am | D | Am | D |
                      Solo

| Am | D G | Am | Am | C G | D |

| C G | D | C G | D | C D ‖

Soul Rebel

Words & Music by
Bob Marley

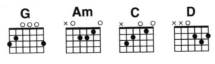

Capo 4th Fret

Intro | Am | Am | G | G |
| Am | Am | G | G N.C. ‖

Chorus 1
       Am   **G**
I'm a rebel, soul rebel.
       Am   **G**
I'm a capturer, soul adventurer.

Verse 1
  G   **Am**
See the morning sun   on the hillside,
C   **D**   **G**
Not living good, yeah,   travel wide.

Said, I'm a living man,
Am
I've got work to do.
C   **D**
If you're not happy, children,
      G
Then you must be blue.

People say:

Chorus 2
     Am
I'm a rebel, let them talk;
  G
Soul rebel, talk won't bother me.
     Am
I'm a capturer, that's what they say.
    G
(Soul adventurer) night and day.

      Am   **G**
(I'm a rebel) I'm a rebel, soul rebel.

Do you hear them, Lippy?

      Am
(I'm a capturer) gossip around the corner.

      G
(Soul adventurer) how they adventure on me, y'all.

Verse 2

G   **Am**
   But see the morning sun   on the hill side,
C   **D**   **G**
   Not living good,   travel wide,

Said, I'm a living man,
Am   **C**   **D**   **G**
   I've got work to do (ooh-ooh, must be blue)

If you're not happy you must be blue.

Chorus 3

      Am   **G**
I'm a rebel, soul rebel;
      Am   **G**
I'm a capturer (ooh-ooh), soul adventurer.

Do you hear me?
      Am   **G**
I'm a rebel, rebel in the morning (soul rebel)

Rebel at midday time. *Fade out*

Substitute

Words & Music by
Pete Townshend

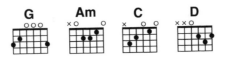

G   Am   C   D

Capo 7th Fret

Intro
  | G   D | C   G | G   D | C   G |

  | G | G | G | G ||

Verse 1
```
G              C              G
You think we look pretty good together,
G              C              G
You think my shoes are made of leather,
```

Pre-chorus 1
```
                 Am
But I'm a substitute for another guy,

I look pretty tall but my heels are high.

The simple things you see are all complicated.
                                        D
I look pretty young but I'm just backdated, yeah.
```

Chorus 1
```
G         D   C        G
(Sub - sti - tute) lies for the fact:
  (G)      D          C     G
I see right through your plastic mac.
  (G)      D          C       G
I look all white but my Dad was black.
    (G)        D          C       G
My fine-looking suit is really made out of sack.
```

Verse 2
```
(G)             C             G
I was born with a plastic spoon in my mouth,
(G)                 C                      G
North side of my town faced east and the east was facing south.
```

Pre-chorus 2

```
                 Am
Dnd now you dare to look me in the eye

But crocodile tears are what you cry.

If it's a genuine problem you won't try

To work it out at all, just pass it by,
          D
Pass it by.
```

Chorus 2

```
G        D    C        G
(Sub - sti - tute) me for him,
G        D        C       G
(Sub - sti - tute) my Coke for gin.
G        D         C        G
(Sub - sti - tute) you fooled my Mum,
  G        D      C       G
At least I'll get my washing done.
```

Solo

```
|: G        | C        | G        | G        :|
```

Pre-chorus 3 As Pre-chorus 1

Link

```
|: G      D | C      G | G      D | C      G :|
```

Verse 3 As Verse 2

Pre-chorus 4 As Pre-chorus 2

Chorus 3 As Chorus 2

Chorus 4 As Chorus 1

Working Class Hero

Words & Music by
John Lennon

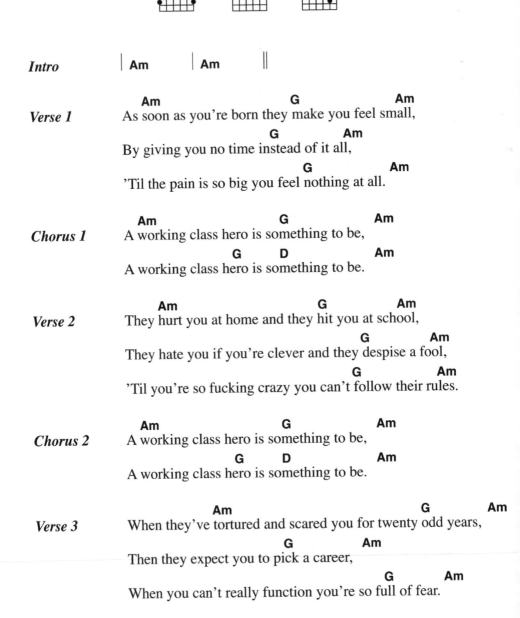

Intro | Am | Am ||

Verse 1
　　　　　　Am　　　　　　　　　　　G　　　　　Am
As soon as you're born they make you feel small,
　　　　　　　　　　　　　　　　G　　　　Am
By giving you no time instead of it all,
　　　　　　　　　　　　　　　　　　G　　　　Am
'Til the pain is so big you feel nothing at all.

Chorus 1
　　　Am　　　　　　　　　　　G　　　　　Am
A working class hero is something to be,
　　　　　　　　　　　　　G　　　D　　　　Am
A working class hero is something to be.

Verse 2
　　　　　Am　　　　　　　　　　　　G　　　　Am
They hurt you at home and they hit you at school,
　　　　　　　　　　　　　　　　　　　G　　　Am
They hate you if you're clever and they despise a fool,
　　　　　　　　　　　　　　　　　　　G　　　Am
'Til you're so fucking crazy you can't follow their rules.

Chorus 2
　　　Am　　　　　　　　　　　G　　　　　Am
A working class hero is something to be,
　　　　　　　　　　　　　G　　　D　　　　Am
A working class hero is something to be.

Verse 3
　　　　　　　Am　　　　　　　　　　　　　　　G　　　Am
When they've tortured and scared you for twenty odd years,
　　　　　　　　　　　　　　　G　　　　Am
Then they expect you to pick a career,
　　　　　　　　　　　　　　　　　　G　　　Am
When you can't really function you're so full of fear.

	Am G Am
Chorus 3	A working class hero is something to be,
	G D Am
	A working class hero is something to be.

	Am G Am
Verse 4	Keep you doped with religion and sex and T. V. ___
	G Am
	And you think you're so clever and classless and free,
	G Am
	But you're still fucking peasants as far as I can see.

	Am G Am
Chorus 4	A working class hero is something to be,
	G D Am
	A working class hero is something to be.

	Am G Am
Verse 5	There's room at the top they are telling you still,
	G Am
	But first you must learn how to smile as you kill,
	G Am
	If you want to be like the folks on the hill.

	Am G Am
Chorus 5	A working class hero is something to be,
	G D Am
	A working class hero is something to be.

	Am G Am
Chorus 6	If you want to be a hero well just follow me,
	G D Am
	If you want to be a hero well just follow me.

Your Love Alone Is Not Enough

Words & Music by
James Dean Bradfield, Nicky Wire & Sean Moore

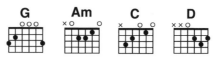

Capo 7th Fret

Verse 1

G   D   Am   G   D   Am
Your love a - lone is not e - nough, not e - nough, not e - nough.

G   D   Am   G
When times get tough, oh, they get tough,

     D   Am
They get tough, they get tough.

C   G   D   Am
Trade all your heroes in for ghosts, in for ghosts, in for ghosts.

C   G
They're always the ones who love you most,

     D   Am   G D Am
Love you most, love you most.

Verse 2

G   D   Am   G   D   Am
Your love a - lone is not e - nough, not e - nough, not e - nough.

G D   Am   G   D   Am
It's what you felt, it's what you said, what you said, what you said

C   G   D   Am
You said the sky would fall on you, fall on you, fall on you.

C   G
Through all the pain your eyes stayed blue,

     D   Am   G D Am
They stayed blue, baby blue.

Link | N.C. ‖

Bridge 1

D   Am   C
But your love alone won't save the world,

                    G   D
You knew the secret of the uni - verse.

                   Am   C
Despite it all you made it worse,

It left you lonely it left you cursed.

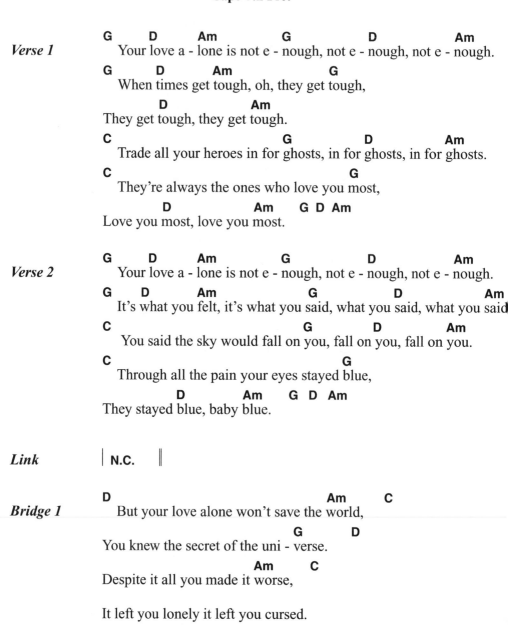

Verse 3

```
G    D      Am               G
You stole the sun straight from my heart,
      D           Am
From my heart, from my heart.
G      D    Am          G        D         Am
With no ex - cuses, just fell a - part, fell a - part, fell a - part.
C                        G         D        Am
No you won't make a mess of me, mess of me, mess of me.
C                              G
For you're as blind as a man can be,
      D        Am    G D Am
Man can be, man can be.
```

| N.C. ‖

Bridge 2

```
D                                Am    C
I could have seen for miles and miles,
                        G    D
I could have made you feel a - live.
                       Am
I could have placed us in e - xile,
                    C
I could have written all your lines.

I could have shown you,
                            G  D  Am
I could have shown you how to cry.
```

Interlude

```
(Am)        G D Am        G D Am
Your love alone    is not enough,
          G D Am              N.C.
Your love alone    is not enough.
```

Instrumental

| D | D | Am | Am |
| C | D | G | G   ‖

Bridge 3

```
D                 Am  C
La, la, la, la, la, la, la, la.
                              G  D  Am
I could have shown you, shown you how to cry.
```

Outro

```
(Am)        G D Am        G D Am
Your love alone    is not enough,
          G D Am
Your love alone.
```

You're Still The One

Words & Music by
Shania Twain & R.J. Lange

Capo 8th Fret

Intro | G | G | C | D ||

Verse 1

G
   Looks like we made it,
C   D
Look how far we've come my baby,
G
   We might have took the long way,
C   D
   We knew we'd get there some day.
G   C   D
   They said, I bet they'll never make it,
             G   C   D
But just look at us holding on.
                  G   C   D   C
We're still together, still going strong.

Chorus 1

G   C
   You're still the one I run to,
Am   D
   The one that I belong to.
G   C   D   C
   You're still the one I want for life.
G   C
   You're still the one that I love,
Am   D
   The only one I dream of.
G   C   D
   You're still the one I kiss goodnight.

Verse 2

G
   Ain't nothing better,
C   D
We beat the odds together.
G
   I'm glad we didn't listen,
C   D
Look at what we would be missing.
G   C   D
   They said, I bet they'll never make it,
       G   C   D
But just look at us holding on.
           G   C   D
We're still together, still going strong.

Chorus 2

G   C
   You're still the one I run to,
Am   D
   The one that I belong to.
G   C   D   C
   You're still the one I want for life.
G   C
   You're still the one that I love,
Am   D
   The only one I dream of.
G   C   D
   You're still the one I kiss goodnight.

You're still the one.

Instrumental ‖: G | C | D | D   :‖

Chorus 3

G   C
   You're still the one I run to,
Am   D
   The one that I belong to.
G   C   D   C
   You're still the one I want for life.
G   C
   You're still the one that I love,
Am   D
   The only one I dream of.
G   C   D
   You're still the one I kiss goodnight.
G
   I'm so glad we made it,
C   D
Look how far we've come baby.

Massachusetts

Words & Music by
Barry Gibb, Maurice Gibb & Robin Gibb

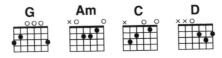

G   Am   C   D

Intro | G | G | G | G ||

Verse 1

G   Am C G
Feel I'm goin' back to Massachusetts,
          Am C   G
Something's telling me I must go home.

                  C
And the lights all went out in Massachusetts
       G   D   G D
The day I left her standing on her own.

Verse 2

G   Am C   G
Tried to hitch a ride to San Francisco,
         Am C G
Gotta do the things I wanna do.

                  C
And the lights all went out in Massachusetts,
         G   D   G D
They brought me back to see my way with you.

Verse 3

G   Am C G
Talk about the life in Massachusetts,
         Am C   G
Speak about the people I have seen.

                  C
And the lights all went out in Massachusetts
        G   D
And Massachusetts is one place I have (seen.)
G   Am   C G   Am   C   G
I will remember Massachusetts...
  seen.   (I will remember Massachusetts.)

    G   Am   C G   Am   C   G
||: I will remember Massachusetts...
              (I will remember Massachusetts.) :||
                       Repeat to fade

3 4 5 6 7
3/09(169